GEO
ART
ANIMALS

Geo Art is a copy and colouring challenge like no other!

Create amazing 3D geometric pictures simply by copying and colouring the shapes on the geometric grids.

This copy and colour challenge will test your colouring skills. Pictures are easy to colour at first then they become trickier as you colour your way through this book.

EASY

Choose one colour and fill in some of the geometric shapes opposite.

Now use different shades of that colour. To create a strong shade, press down hard. Press lightly to colour some shapes in a lighter shade. Carry on colouring until you complete the picture.

Does the heart now seem 3D?

To complete the pictures in this section you will need to use different shades of one or two colours.

Copy the colour from the finished picture on the left, then colour in the empty shapes in each picture on the right.

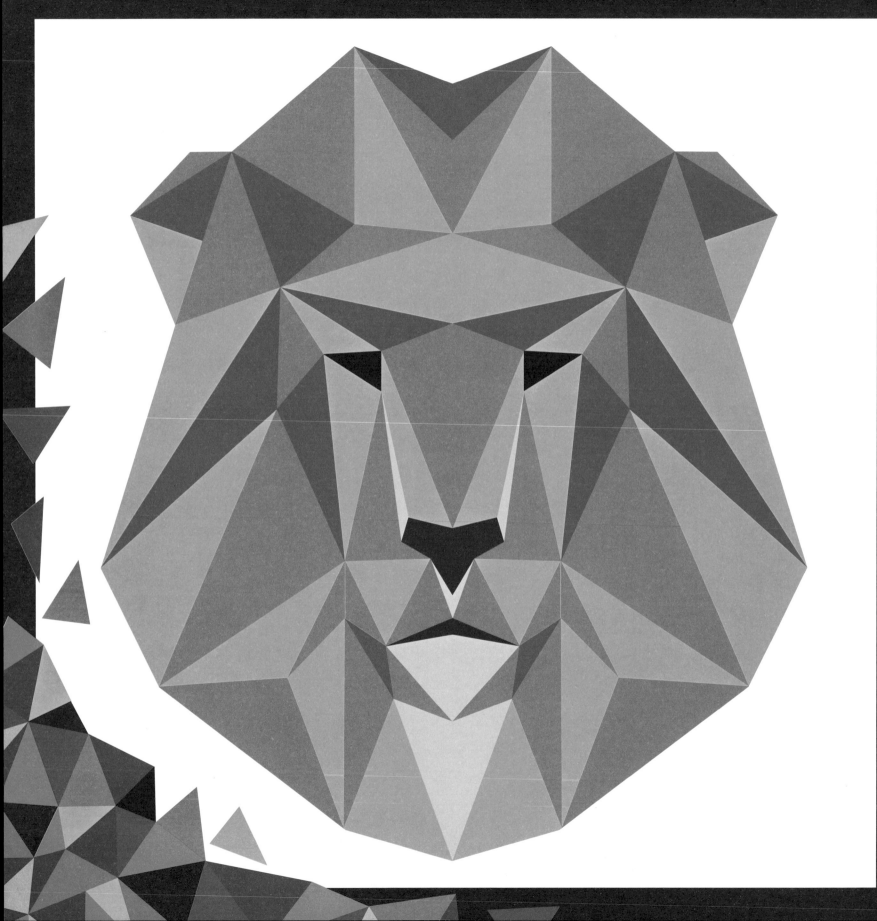

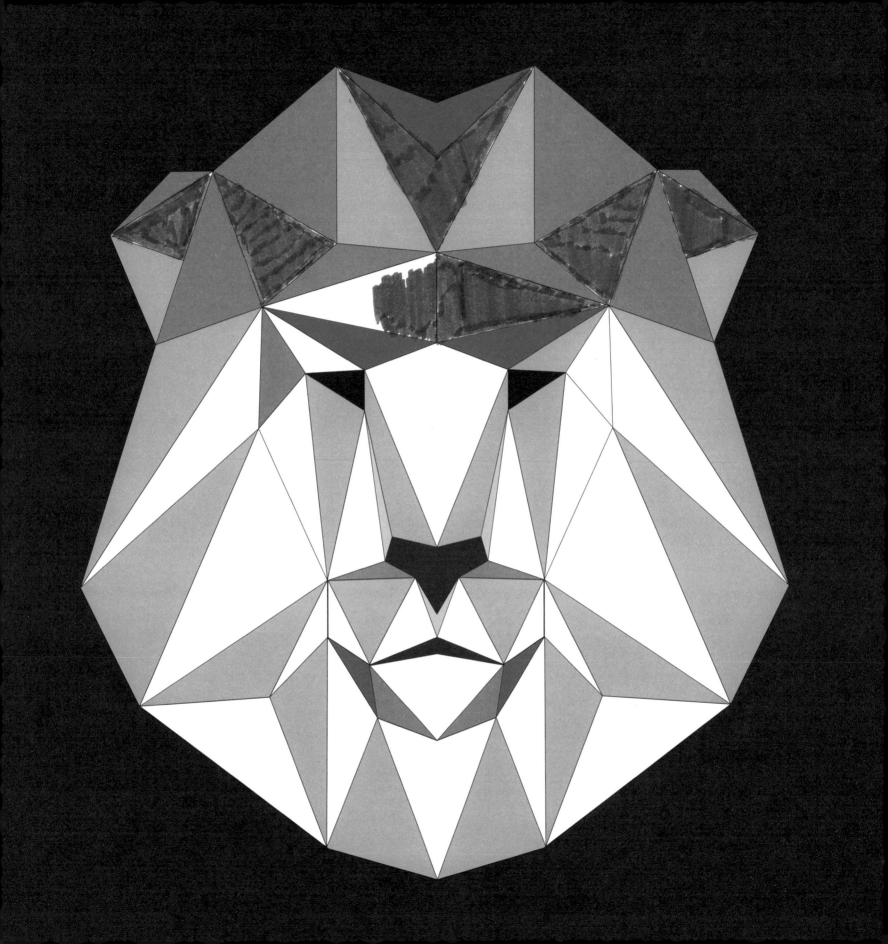

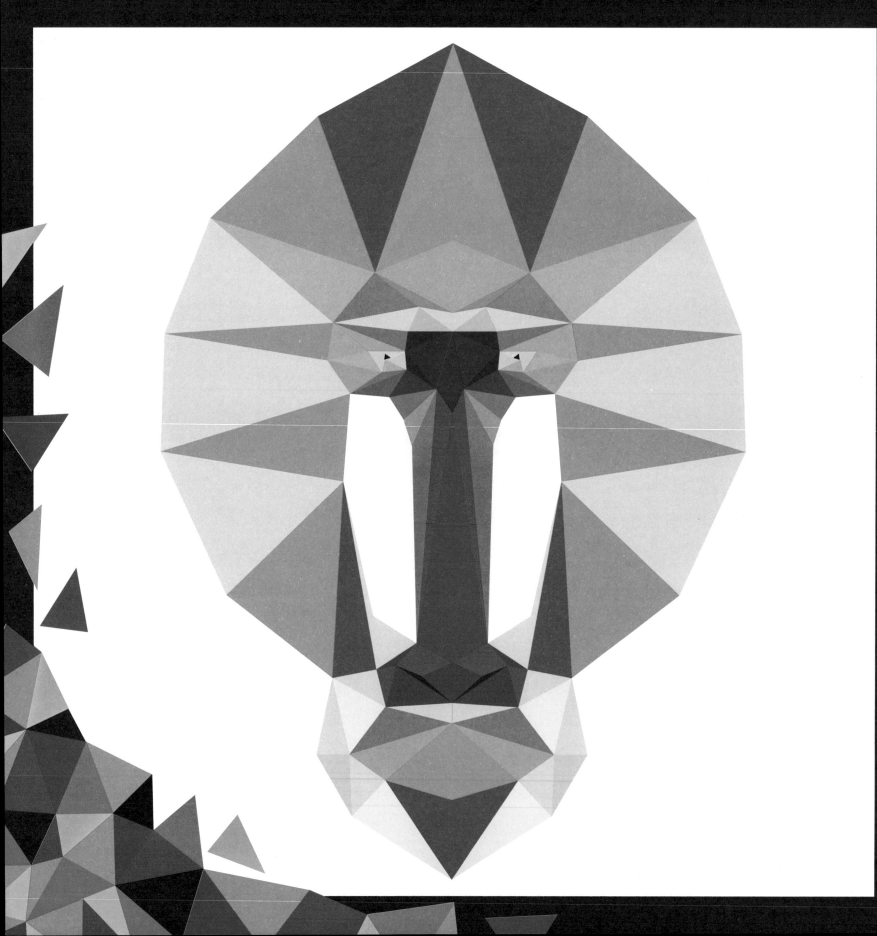

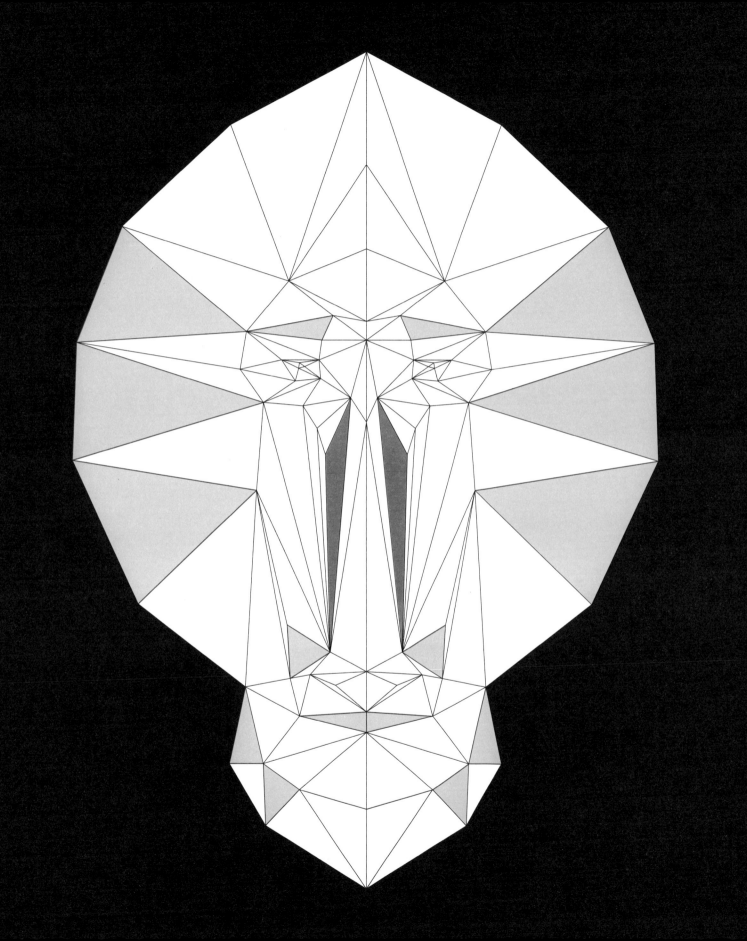

TRICKY

Use different shades of
yellow, orange and brown
to colour this fish.

In this section, the colouring
challenges become a little trickier.
There are more geometric shapes
to copy and more colours to use for
each picture.

Copy the pictures, and choose and
colour each shape carefully.

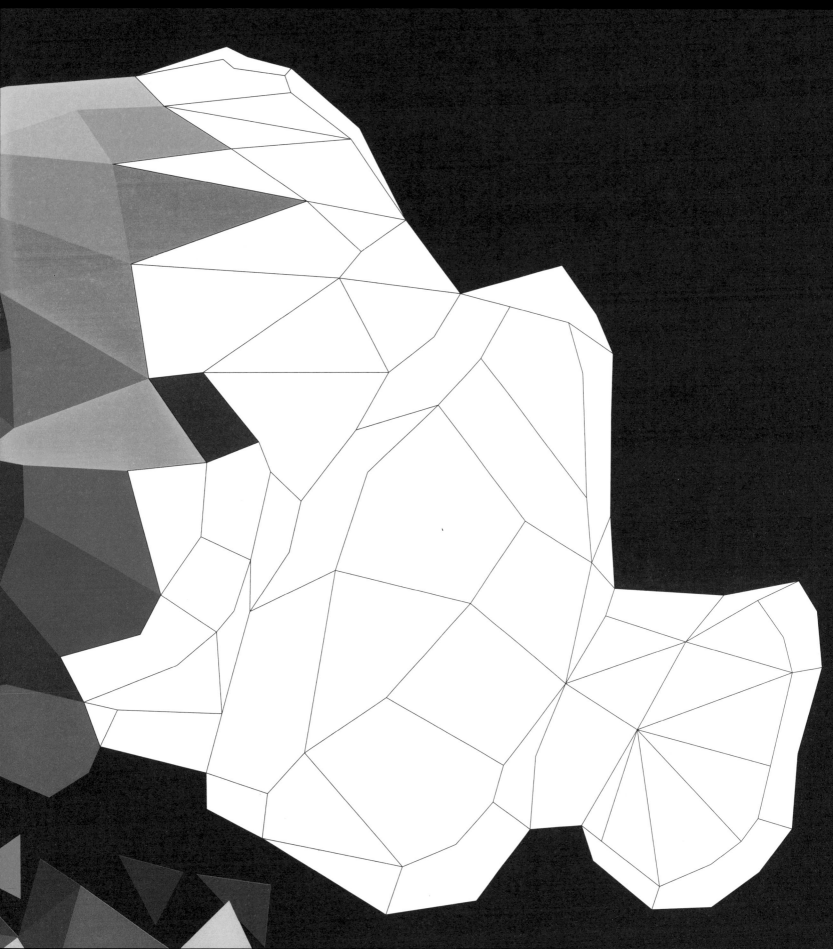

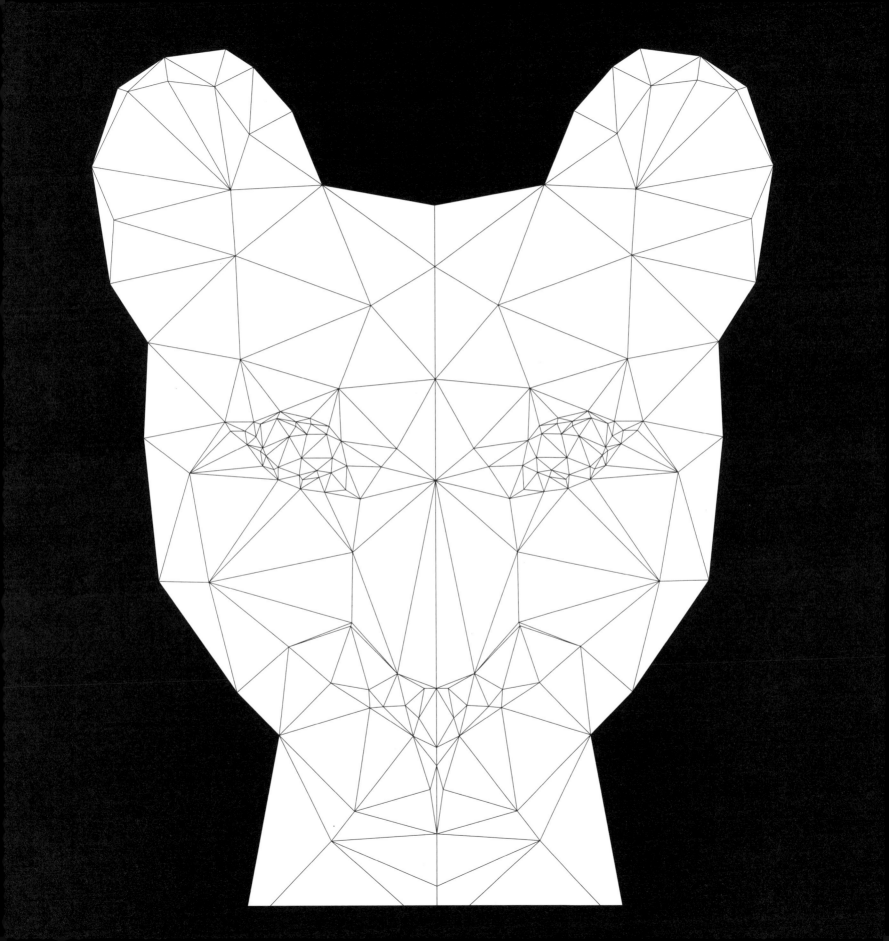

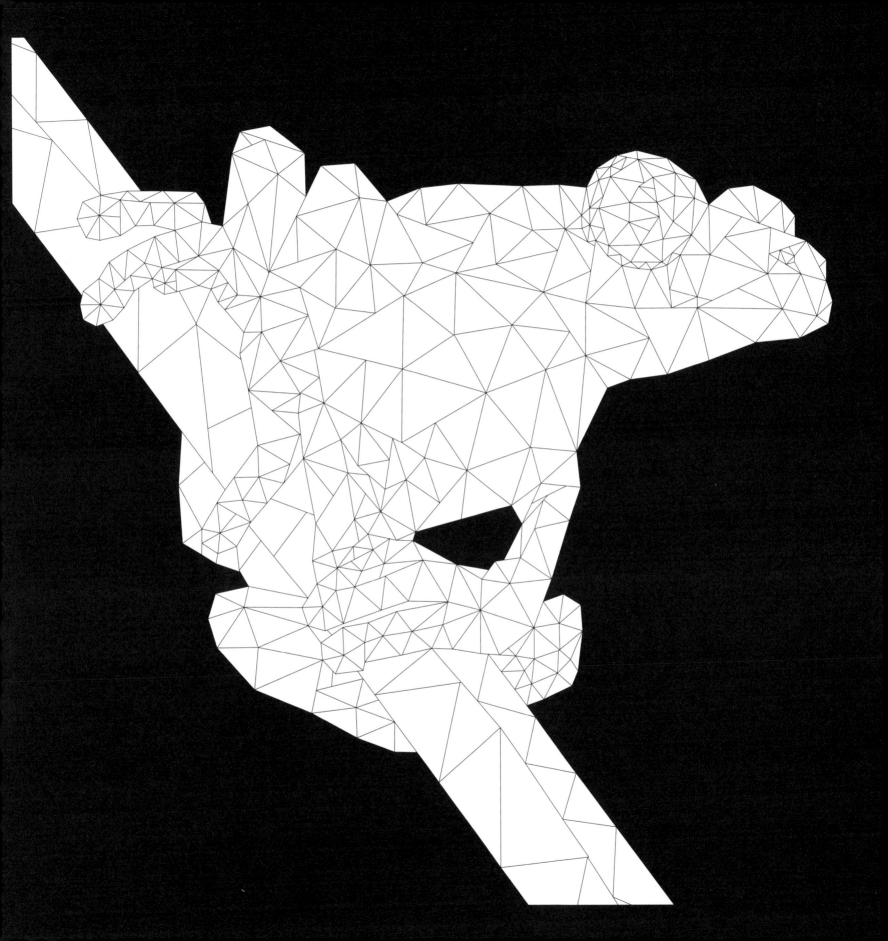

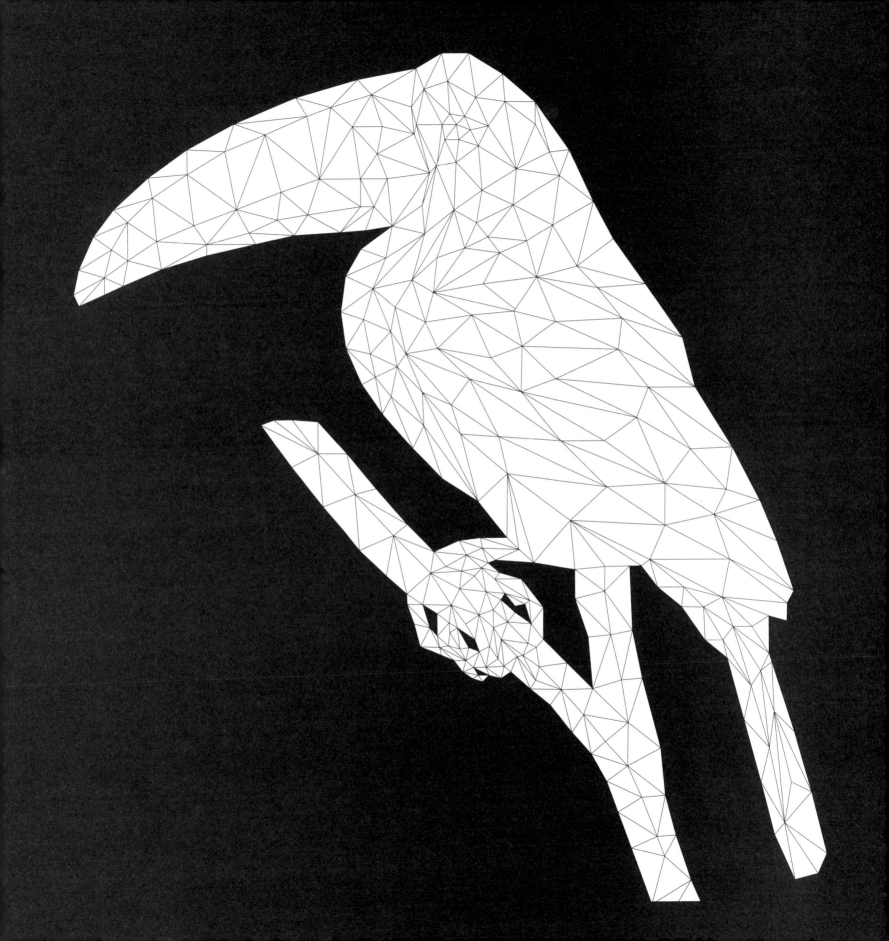

TOUGH

The colouring challenge
gets tougher in this section!

The copy and colour pictures are
now made up of lots of different-sized
geometric shapes, with lots more
colours to use on the geometric grid.

Start with one detail, such as an eye, and
colour each shape one at a time. Remember
to choose and colour each shape carefully.

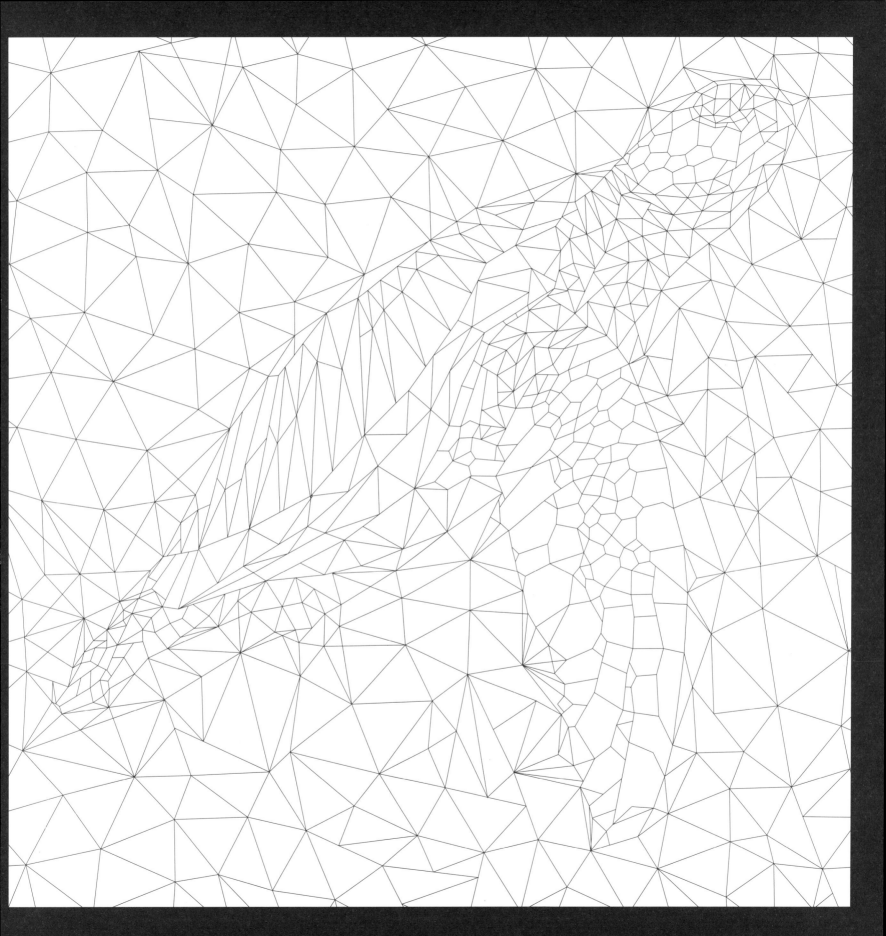

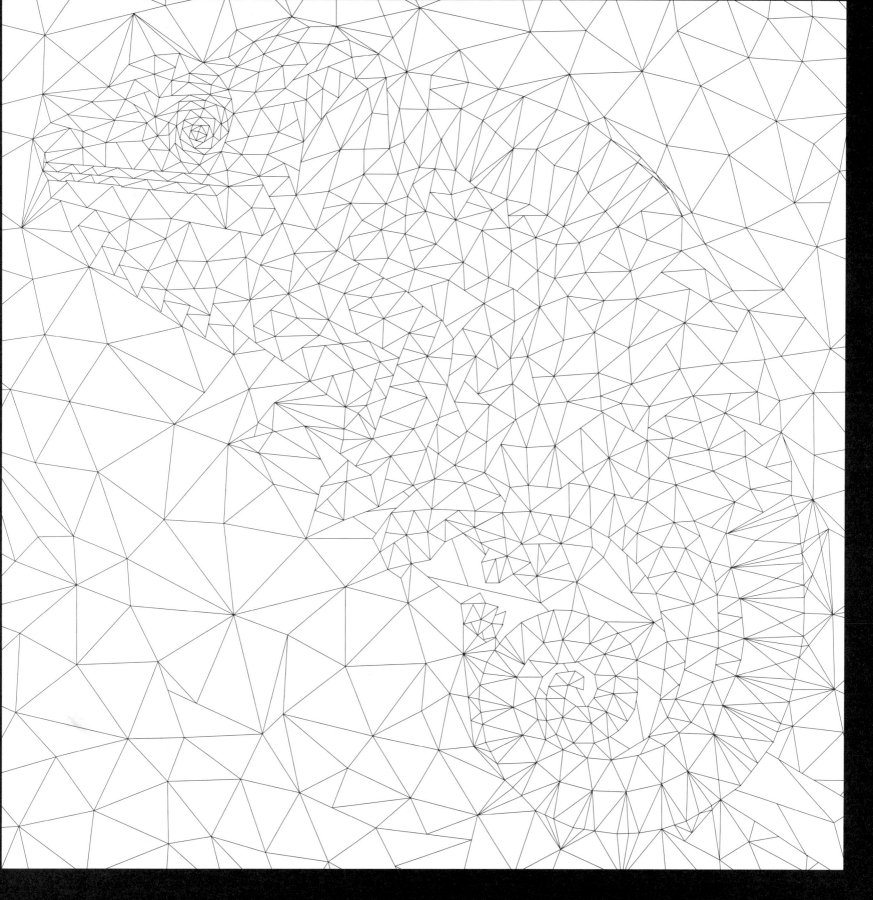

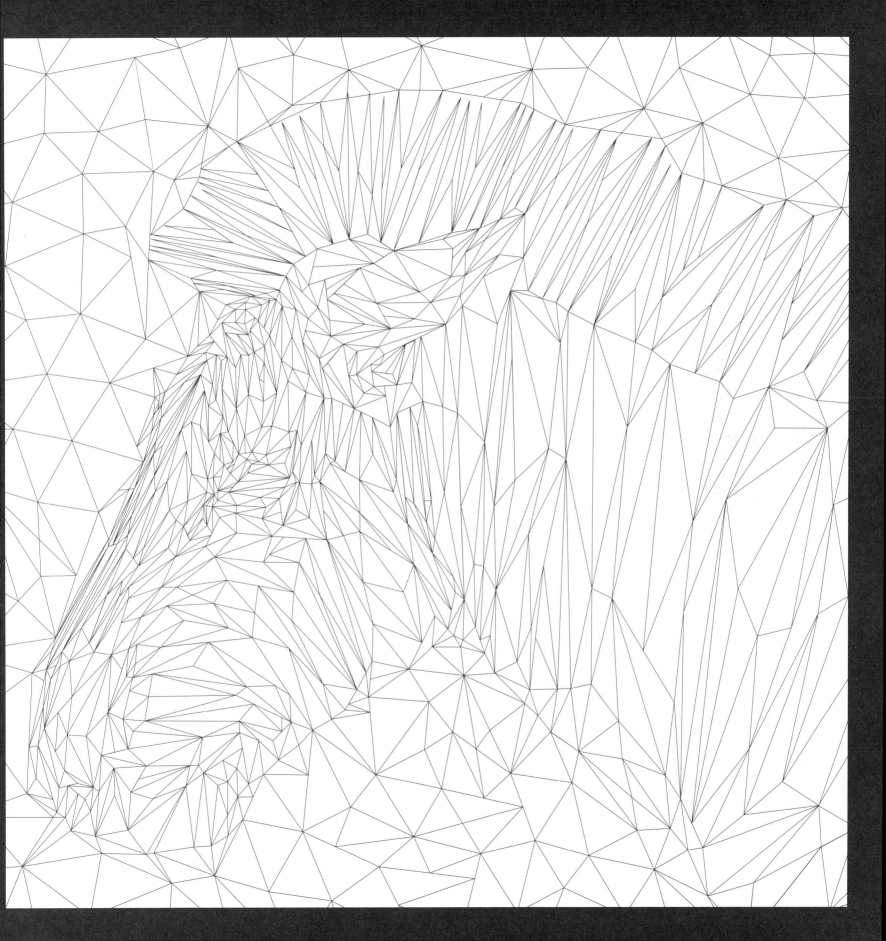

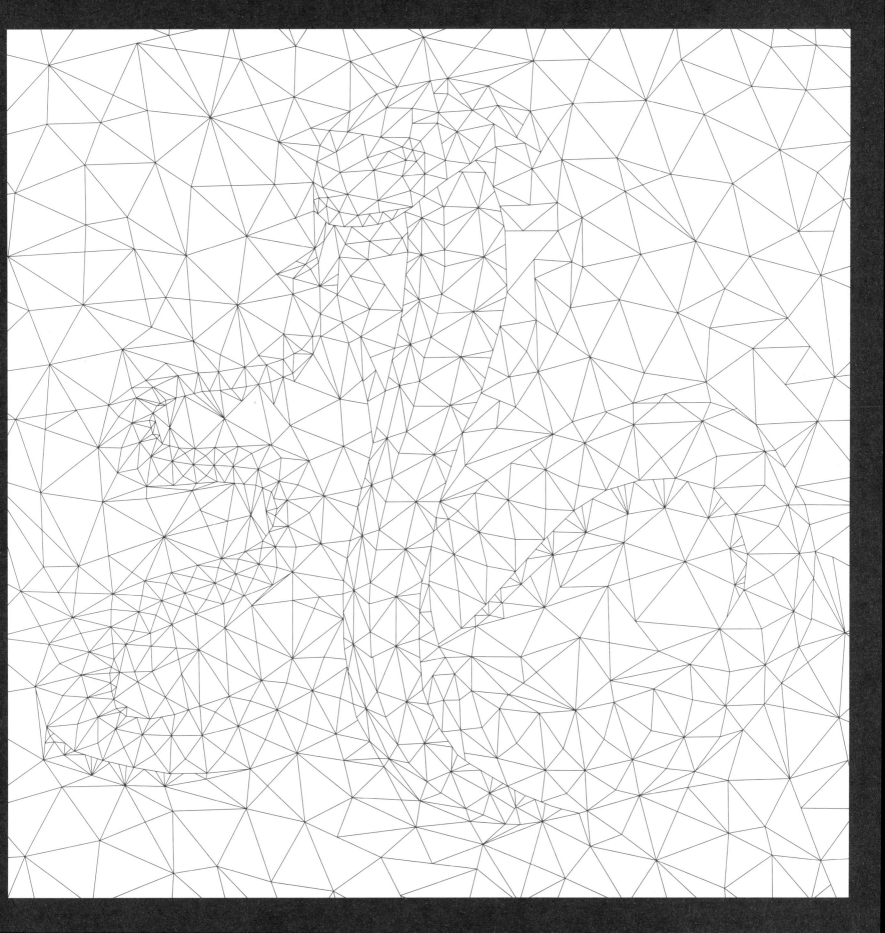

GEO ART

The following pages are for you to create your own *Geo Art* pictures.

There are seven pages of geometric grids for you to colour and create your own pictures out of the geometric shapes.

Use your imagination to create any image you wish, and use colours and add in lines to create smaller shapes for extra detail.